The DBT Workbook
for Teens

Mindfulness and Emotion Regulation Techniques for Overcoming Stress and Negative Thoughts

Richard Bass

Receive a FREE Planner for Kids
by scanning below!

Table of Contents

Introduction

The first step to changing our relationship to feelings is to be curious about them and the messages they send to us. —
Lane Pederson

Surviving the teenage years is a lot harder today than it was several decades ago. Besides the pressures to perform at school, navigate relationships, or discover who they are, modern teenagers are exposed to threats like school shootings, racial profiling, domestic abuse, and peer pressure, which cause a lot of stress.

Unfortunately, many teenagers don't have the necessary psychological tools to cope with these challenges. For example, some teens don't know how to manage triggers and de-escalate stressful situations, while others don't know how to communicate their hurt feelings without becoming aggressive or setting firm and healthy boundaries.

That is where dialectical behavioral therapy (DBT) and this workbook come into effect. DBT is a type of psychotherapy that seeks to improve the way adults and teenagers deal with stress. By focusing on two factors—change and acceptance—this therapy can encourage teenagers to

- adopt healthy coping behaviors

- learn how to manage those "big feelings"

- calm their mind and body during heated moments

- improve their communication skills

The purpose of this workbook is to teach boys and girls aged 13–19, how to cope with stress, anxiety, and strong emotions by practicing the four DBT skills of mindfulness, distress tolerance, emotion regulation, and interpersonal effectiveness.

Since the 1970s, people have been using DBT to learn to manage stressors and treat symptoms of mental health conditions like generalized anxiety disorder (GAD), depression, borderline personality disorder, and suicidal behaviors. Celebrities have also come out and expressed how helpful this therapy has been for maintaining mental wellness.

For instance, singer and actress Lady Gaga told Oprah Winfrey during an interview that DBT was a part of her mental health regimen, and in *Teen Vogue* magazine, Selena Gomez shared how DBT changed her life for the better and believed it should be a subject taught in schools (Tsangarides, 2023).

The same life-changing DBT skills that have been praised by thousands of people can be found in the following chapters. After going through this workbook, teenagers will feel prepared to handle stressful situations at home, school, and amongst their peer groups. They will be able to understand that their emotions and behaviors are within their control, and therefore can be adjusted to achieve positive outcomes.

However, before we go into the exercises, it is important to get a better understanding of what DBT entails, and how it can enhance the quality of your life!

Chapter 1:

What Is Dialectical Behavioral Therapy?

In dialectical behavior therapy, the balance is between change and acceptance. You need to change the behaviors in your life that are creating more suffering for yourself and others while simultaneously also accepting yourself the way you are. –
Matthew McKay

Defining DBT

Dialectical behavioral therapy (DBT) is a type of psychotherapy that falls under the umbrella of cognitive behavioral therapy (CBT). However, what makes it different from CBT is the fact that it focuses on two factors that can bring healing: change and acceptance.

Change is the ability to assess your current thoughts, feelings, and lifestyle choices and be honest about what you need to let go of in order to live a healthy and vibrant life. The fact of the matter is that not every thought, emotion, or habit is beneficial to your well-being, and sometimes, holding onto these harmful things can increase stress and anxiety.

Acceptance, on the other hand, is about coming to terms with the way your life is right now, instead of trying to run away or avoid facing your current circumstances. Accepting reality is not easy, especially when you have other plans or hopes for your life. However, only after you have come to accept your life—as good or bad as it may be—can you actually change those things within your control.

The therapy was originally created in the 1980s by Dr. Marsha Linehan. She discovered it after completing a clinical trial of patients with borderline personality disorder. The therapy proved successful in combating depression and suicidal thinking, but later on, research found that DBT can be used to treat symptoms related to other mental health conditions, such as anxiety, depression, self-harm, substance abuse, and eating disorders (Schimelpfening, 2023).

What Are the Benefits of DBT?

You may have tried various forms of psychotherapy before, like talk therapy where you speak directly to a therapist. The benefit of DBT is that it can be practiced alongside other therapeutic techniques, so you don't need to feel like you must pick one or the other!

Nonetheless, DBT is one of the best therapies for stress management. It won't magically make the stress disappear, but it can teach you various ways to cope with stress without compromising your well-being. During the teenage years, you start to learn about the highs and lows of life; sometimes, things are looking up for you and your family, and other times, they aren't.

Difficult moments in life can be overwhelming when you aren't equipped with the proper coping strategies. In extreme cases, they can even change how you see yourself or interact with other people. DBT teaches four skills that you can turn to whenever you are feeling frustrated by life. The four skills enable you to remain calm, recognize how you are feeling, think clearly about positive steps to take, and express your thoughts and feelings with confidence.

The Four DBT Skills

DBT centers around teaching four skills: mindfulness, emotion regulation, distress tolerance, and interpersonal effectiveness. Each skill targets a specific component of stress management. The purpose of this workbook is to introduce each skill and a variety of exercises that you can practice in the comfort of your home.

Here is a brief overview of the four DBT skills:

Mindfulness

Mindfulness is the practice of paying attention to what is happening in the present moment. Oftentimes, what gets you upset are thoughts related to past hurts or unknown future events. But when your mind is resting in the present moment, you will notice that you feel calm and in control. Mindfulness skills are great to use when you are caught up in a stressful situation and desire to bring your mind and body back to a relaxed state.

Emotion Regulation

Everybody gets frustrated at times, but not everybody knows how to handle their frustration. Emotion regulation is the practice of recognizing, describing, and controlling big emotions like anger, fear, sadness, or loneliness. Emotion regulation skills come in handy when you have been triggered by an upsetting situation, but don't know how to process what you are feeling.

Distress Tolerance

Distress tolerance refers to your ability to remain resilient during difficult times. When your distress tolerance is low, you tend to respond to stress by becoming aggressive, emotionally withdrawing, or mentally checking out. These strategies may feel like a big relief in the moment, but they reinforce bad habits, like teaching you to avoid stress instead of standing tall and overcoming it. DBT distress tolerance skills seek to increase your tolerance levels for stress and adopt healthy coping strategies during crises.

Interpersonal Effectiveness

Another source of stress is the inability to stand up for yourself when you are feeling disrespected or violated. Interpersonal effectiveness skills show you various ways to positively communicate your thoughts and feelings, so that you can express concerns, demand respect from others, and set healthy boundaries that make you feel safe in every relationship.

How to Use This Workbook

The following chapters present a range of exercises that reinforce the four DBT skills. You are welcome to select which exercises you would like to practice, and in what order. Please note that while DBT is often administered by a qualified therapist, various DBT exercises are safe to practice at home. If you have concerns about some of the exercises mentioned in this workbook, please consult your doctor before continuing with them.

The exercises you are about to read are effective stress management tools. Nevertheless, to gain the full benefits from each exercise, you will need to practice, practice, practice!

Chapter 2:

Mindfulness Skills

If it's out of your hands, it deserves freedom from your mind too. –Ivan Nuru

What Is Mindfulness?

Have you ever been told by someone to be mindful? In essence, what they were asking you to do is pay attention. The word "mindful" comes from the term "mindfulness", which describes the practice of bringing your awareness to what is happening right now.

You might be wondering what the big fuss around mindfulness is about. When faced with a stressful situation, the logical area of the brain switches off, and the amygdala—the part of your brain that senses danger—is activated. You may notice that you are overwhelmed with fear and cannot think clearly about what to do.

This is when practicing mindfulness can be a game-changer. In the heat of the moment, when your stress levels are high, mindfulness skills can help you calm down and regain control of your mind. By encouraging you to focus on the present moment, you can break the cycle of overthinking or obsessing over negative thoughts.

The exercises below will introduce you to three DBT mindfulness skills: observation, describing, and participation.

Observation Skills

Observing is the practice of noticing what is happening, without making any judgments. You are encouraged to pick up on any thoughts that may be entering your mind, any sensations that may be going through your body, or any action you may be noticing with your senses.

What makes observation powerful is that it has a soothing effect. Instead of noticing and formulating opinions, you simply allow things to exist without attempting to make sense of them. In other words, you embrace the pleasant and unpleasant thoughts or sensations you feel, until they naturally disappear.

Complete the following exercises to sharpen your observation skills:

Exercise 1: Object Fascination

One of the simplest ways to practice observation is to focus on an object. However, instead of just seeing the object from a one-dimensional point of view, take the time to analyze it from different angles.

For example, if you are observing a chair, notice different characteristics, such as height, size, color, texture, weight, design, and shape. If your object has sound or can be eaten, engage your sense of hearing and taste and make more observations.

Make a list of your observations on the line space provided below:

_____

_____

_____

_____

_____

_____

_____

_____

_____

Exercise 2: Be the Observer

Overthinking is an unhealthy habit that can increase stress and anxiety. The cycle typically starts with an unwanted thought that is replayed over and over again in your mind. Practicing observation can help you break free from overthinking. This is because it creates enough distance between you and the unpleasant thought.

For instance, instead of actively engaging with an unwanted thought and seeking to know more about what it is and where it comes from, you can take a step back and play the role of the observer, the one who has no emotional attachment to any passing thought. The observer notices an incoming thought but doesn't interfere with it. They say, "I am thinking about this, but I don't need to look deeply into it."

To practice observing your thoughts, follow the instructions below:

- Close your eyes and take three deep breaths.

- Imagine that you have gained exclusive access into your mind. Find a comfortable place to sit where you can observe your passing thoughts.

- Patiently wait for a thought to enter your mind. Don't feel pressure if minutes go by without noticing any thought.

- When a thought enters your mind, notice what kind of thought it is. Is it a pleasant or unpleasant thought? Urgent or non-urgent thought? A soothing or stressful thought?

- After observing what kind of thought it is, gently say to yourself, "I am experiencing a pleasant/unpleasant thought"—depending on what it is.

- Now that you have acknowledged what kind of thought you are experiencing, don't look any deeper into it. Simply allow the thought to roam in your mind until it naturally goes away.

- Shift your attention to another thought that has entered your mind and repeat the same steps.

How did you find the exercise? Record your experience below:

_____

_____

_____

_____

_____

_____

_____

_____

Exercise 3: Listen to Your Body

Your body is constantly sending information to your brain about what is happening in your environment. This is how your body keeps you alive! In general, your brain will activate the stress response after receiving information from your body that you are in potential danger. Afterward, you will go into "fight-flight-freeze" mode to get away from the threat.

Being able to observe body sensations can help you pick up on the signs of stress and act quickly, before your brain activates the stress response. Your body is constantly sending information, and all you need to do is listen. About once or twice a day, or whenever you enter new environments, complete a quick body scan to sense what your body is experiencing.

You can choose to either lie down on a flat surface or sit on a comfortable chair. Start at the crown of your head and slowly work your way down. Spend between 30 seconds to a minute on each body part and ask yourself: How does it feel? Notice if the part of your body has a positive or negative sensation. If the sensation is negative, notice whether it is a physical or an emotional tension or pain.

For example, shortly after walking into the exam room, you might feel a negative sensation around the chest area. Your heart rate may be beating really fast and making you feel uncomfortable. Upon further observation, you might notice that the discomfort you feel is emotional rather than physical. Perhaps due to not feeling confident about the exam you are about to write, you are starting to feel anxious.

Complete a full-body scan and record the body sensations you pick up below. Practice distinguishing positive sensations from negative sensations, and physical discomfort from emotional discomfort.

_____

_____

_____

_____

_____

_____

_____

_____

Describing Skills

Describing what you are thinking or feeling usually occurs immediately after you have made observations. Once again, you are given the task of simply describing your experience without making any judgments or forming opinions. Describing skills are important because they can help you understand what is going through your mind and body. With more understanding, you are less likely to go into a panic.

Complete the following exercises to sharpen your describing skills:

Exercise 4: Zone in on Your Emotions

Have you ever felt a strong emotion, but couldn't describe what it was or how it made you feel? This can be frustrating, especially when the emotion starts to grow bigger and take control of your mind. Learning how to describe your emotions is the first step to taking back control and managing stress.

Begin the exercise by choosing an emotion from the table below that you would like to focus on. It can be a pleasant or unpleasant emotion, something you have felt recently, or something you felt a while ago.

Pleasant Emotions	Unpleasant Emotions
Excited	Lonely
Strong	Jealous
Loving	Annoyed
Energetic	Bored
Proud	Shy

The next step is to describe the emotion using various creative methods, such as:

1. Describe the emotion by drawing a picture.

2. Describe the emotion by listing actions that are associated with it.

3. Describe the emotion's intensity on a scale of 0 to 10, with 10 being the most intense.

4. Describe the emotion by writing down thoughts that are triggered whenever it arises.

Here is an example using the emotion of loneliness:

1. Loneliness as a drawing:

2. Actions associated with loneliness: Isolating from people, sleeping a lot, listening to sad music, etc.

3. The intensity of loneliness from a scale of 0 to 10: 6

4. Thoughts triggered by loneliness: "Nobody wants to be around me," "Something is wrong with me," etc.

Now it is your turn. Choose an emotion and describe it using the four creative methods.

_____

_____

_____

_____

_____

_____

_____

_____

_____

_____

_____

Exercise 5: Make Mental Notes

When you feel pressure on your mind due to excessive thinking, grab a notebook and pen and describe the thoughts running across your mind. This is helpful for two reasons. First, it allows you to regain control of your mind by slowing down your thinking and focusing on specific thoughts. Second, the simple act of offloading worrying thoughts onto paper can alleviate stress and help you think clearly about your options.

Below is a basic table format that you can use to make mental notes:

Date	What are you thinking?	How does it make you feel?	What does it make you want to do?

Exercise 6: "I Feel" Statements

When expressing how you feel, it is important to take ownership of your emotional experience. Use observation skills to notice that the strong emotion is bubbling up from within you, and describing skills to let others know exactly how you feel.

One of the recommendations that therapists make is to use "I feel" statements, rather than "you" statements. The "I" allows you to take ownership and prevent the other person from being defensive, which makes it easier to describe your emotions.

Here are examples of "you" vs. "I feel" statements:

You: You never allow me to speak without interrupting me.

I feel: I feel frustrated when I am interrupted while speaking.

You: You never text me unless I text you first.

I feel: I feel taken for granted when I am the one who regularly texts first.

Next to each "you" statement below, write down the alternative "I feel" statement:

"You" Statement	"I Feel" Statement
You are constantly on my case about doing homework!	
You don't contribute anything to the team project.	
You don't respect my privacy.	
You keep on repeating the same instructions!	
You never let me make my own decisions.	
You always think the worst of me.	

Participation Skills

Participation is about focusing wholeheartedly on an action taking place. It could be something as basic as paying attention to the motion of your toothbrush while brushing your teeth or being aware of your breathing rhythm as you inhale and exhale. What makes DBT participation skills effective is that they allow you to let go of troubling thoughts, judgments, or anything that might take your focus away from what is happening right here, right now. You may notice a sudden improvement in your moods whenever you practice these skills.

Complete the following exercises to sharpen your participation skills:

Exercise 7: Mindful Breathing

Whenever you are feeling stressed, you will notice that your breathing rate changes. Instead of the regular pace and rhythm, it may start to accelerate and become unstable. Mindful breathing is a relaxation technique that encourages you to regain control of your breathing during stressful situations by taking slow and deep breaths.

Practicing this technique can reverse symptoms of stress like shortness of breath, accelerating heartbeat, and tightness of the chest. It can also leave you feeling incredibly calm since the slow and deep breaths allow more oxygen to the brain.

Below is a short meditation script to teach you the fundamental steps of mindful breathing:

- Lie down in a comfortable position and close your eyes.

- Take a slow and deep breath through your nose for four counts, hold your breath for one count, then gently release the air out of your mouth for another four counts.

- Notice any changes to your body.

- Repeat the sequence, but this time place one hand on your chest and another on your belly. As you inhale, notice the hand on your belly rising up. Ensure the hand on your chest remains still. As you exhale, notice the hand on your belly returning to normal position; the other hand should still remain still.

- Notice any changes to your body.

- Repeat the sequence again, but this time imagine that you are inhaling a positive emotion you desire to experience and exhaling a negative emotion that is trapped in your body. For example, you can imagine inhaling freedom and exhaling anger.

- Notice any changes to your body, then when you are ready, open your eyes.

Exercise 8: Activate Wise Mind

"Wise mind" is a DBT term that was created by Dr. Linehan to describe the point where emotional thinking meets logical thinking. Instead of interpreting what is happening around you from a place of feelings or strictly on facts, you can practice looking for wisdom.

One of the ways to do this is to think of someone, dead or alive, who you label as a wise person. This could be a friend, family member, teacher, coach, or influential figure. Ask yourself: "What would that person think or act in this situation?" This kind of question can activate your wise mind and help you find clever solutions to your problems.

Think of a situation that has been worrying you over the past week or month. Imagine that you could ask a wise person for advice on how to respond to the situation. If it helps, close your eyes and imagine you are having a one-on-one meeting with this wise person, and they are sharing information about what to do. Listen carefully to what the wise person intuitively tells you. Write down every idea, thought, or bit of advice that enters your mind.

_____

_____

_____

_____

_____

_____

_____

_____

_____

Exercise 9: Let Go of Negative Judgments

Naturally, observations lead to judgments. Part of the work of the human brain is to encode and analyze information by assigning labels and categories. For example, if you get a low grade on a test, you might judge yourself as being lazy, unfocused, or less smart than the other kids.

The trouble with judgments comes when they are negative and charged with emotion. When this occurs, you are unable to think clearly and take positive action. Your negative judgments might discourage you, if they are directed at you, or cause you to think poorly of others. Letting go of negative judgments starts with acknowledging when you are having them and understanding how they make you feel or what they make you want to do.

Below is a table you can use to record negative judgments whenever they enter your mind. In each column, note the situation that led to the judgment, the negative judgment you made, how it made you feel—the immediate urge you felt—and the outcome of the situation. As time goes on, and you become more aware of your negative judgments, observe how the outcomes positively change.

Date	What happened?	What negative judgment did you make?	How did you feel/what urge came over you?	What was the outcome?

The exercises above have given you a glimpse of what DBT mindfulness skills involve. The main point to remember is that shifting your attention to the present moment can help you escape mental traps like overthinking or obsessive worrying. Three ways to practice being present are observing what is happening within and around you, describing what you observe, and paying undivided attention to whatever thought or behavior—whether good or bad—that is emerging.

Chapter 3:

Emotion Regulation Skills

Rejecting emotions or trying to push them away usually intensifies them. If the message is not heard, it needs to get louder.
–Lane Pederson

What Is Emotion Regulation?

Emotions are a normal part of life. Sometimes you will feel up and other times you will feel down. Emotion regulation is the ability to control the effects emotions have on you. Whether you are feeling up or down, you are able to remain calm and level-headed.

Emotion regulation skills are a necessary component of stress management. They enable you to recognize strong emotions, like anger or sadness, and find healthy ways to release emotional tension from your body. With your emotions in check, you can feel more confident to face present challenges!

The exercises below will help you practice three DBT emotion regulation skills: recognizing emotions, accepting strong emotions, and taking the opposite action. Some of these exercises may trigger intense emotions. Remember to go through each exercise at your own pace and take slow and deep breaths during uncomfortable moments.

Recognize Your Emotions

The brain is wired to interpret life events by how they make you feel. Life events that make you feel happy, such as spending time with your friends, are interpreted as safe and pleasurable experiences. On the contrary, life events that make you feel afraid, such as being bullied or yelled at, are interpreted as threatening.

Learning how to recognize your emotions can help you understand how different life events make you feel. With this information, you can prepare in advance for stressful events or avoid situations or people that make you feel uncomfortable. The better you get at recognizing your emotions, the more control you will have over them.

Complete the following exercises to practice recognizing different emotions:

Exercise 10: Track an Emotion

How much do you know about your emotions? For one week, challenge yourself to track seven different emotions each day. Pick an emotion to track and for 24 hours, notice how many times it arises, and what kinds of situations trigger it. If you are tracking the emotion of frustration, for example, it might be triggered when you attend your least favorite class, when you feel hungry, or when your parents remind you to complete house chores.

Record your notes in the table below:

Day	Emotion	Trigger Situations
Monday		

Day	Emotion	Trigger Situations
Tuesday		
Wednesday		
Thursday		
Friday		
Saturday		
Sunday		

Exercise 11: Expand Your Emotions Vocabulary

Sometimes emotions can feel confusing because you cannot find the correct word to label how you are feeling. Expanding your emotions vocabulary can make it easier to recognize complicated emotions. However, before expanding your vocabulary, it is important to tell the difference between primary and secondary emotions.

There are six primary emotions and hundreds of secondary emotions that fall under these six categories. When you detect an emotion, the first step is to recognize which primary emotion is being triggered, thereafter you can find a secondary emotion that best describes how you are feeling.

Consider the list of primary and secondary emotions below then answer the questions; ensure you pick both from the same category.

Anger	Surprise	Disgust	Happiness	Fear	Sadness
Frustrated	Confused	Judgmental	Content	Scared	Lonely
Critical	Amazed	Embarrassed	Playful	Anxious	Hurt
Let down	Shocked	Disappointed	Peaceful	Rejected	Isolated
Bitter	Excited	Repelled	Thankful	Threatened	Ashamed
Jealous	Energetic	Disapproving	Confident	Insecure	Fragile
Disrespected	Eager	Horrified	Hopeful	Inferior	Depressed

1. Pick a primary and secondary emotion and describe how you feel about the future.

_____

_____

_____

_____

2. Pick a primary and secondary emotion and describe your relationship with your parents or siblings.

_____

_____

_____

_____

3. Pick a primary and secondary emotion and describe your relationship with friends.

_____

_____

_____

_____

4. Think about a situation that made you feel two conflicting emotions at the same time—e.g., happy and sad. Write down what happened and the two conflicting emotions you felt.

_____

_____

_____

_____

5. Think about a situation that changed the way you feel over time—e.g., started feeling angry and then felt disgusted after some time. Write down what happened and how your emotions changed over time.

_____

_____

_____

_____

Exercise 12: Interpreting Song Lyrics

There are some songs that can express your emotions better than you can. Pick one of your favorite songs that captures an emotion you have felt recently. Focus on a specific section of the song that you connect with the most. Write a short paragraph or two about what those words mean to you. Perhaps you have overcome a similar situation and can relate to the artist's experience.

_____

_____

_____

_____

_____

_____

_____

_____

Accept Strong Emotions

When you don't have a healthy relationship with your emotions, you may learn to reject or avoid unpleasant feelings. For instance, instead of taking the time to observe and describe what you are feeling, you might immediately shut down or push the unpleasant feelings away. Over time, this can make it difficult to process and address unpleasant feelings in a healthy way.

Accepting strong emotions is about learning to be comfortable with uncomfortable feelings. When they arise, you can practice empathizing with how you feel, rather than seeking to immediately get rid of them. Over time, this simple practice can improve your relationship with your emotions and help you stabilize your moods.

Complete the following exercises to practice accepting strong emotions:

Exercise 13: Ride the Wave

Have you ever watched a wave form? At first, you notice the water volume increasing, until eventually the body of water grows in size, reaches the breaking point, then comes toppling back down.

Strong emotions form similarly to waves. You might sense the emotion bubbling inside of you, growing in size, reaching its breaking point, then gradually calming down until you cannot feel it anymore.

You can practice accepting strong emotions by learning to ride the emotional waves. Here are simple steps to follow:

- Pick an intense emotion that you feel regularly. This could be anger, sadness, or loneliness.

- Close your eyes and recall a past memory where you felt the same emotion.

- Play back the memory from start to finish. Focus on how the emotion began, how it grew in size, reached the final breaking point, and how it slowly subsided.

- Repeat the memory sequence again and ride the wave. Continue to ride the wave until you start feeling comfortable with the intensity of the emotion.

- Remember to take slow and deep breaths while playing back the memory. Note that you can pause the memory or discontinue it whenever you want.

How did you find the exercise? Record your experience below:

_____

_____

_____

_____

Exercise 14: Validate Your Emotions

Validating your emotions is about accepting what you are feeling without judging whether it is good or bad, acceptable or unacceptable. Accepting how you are feeling can reduce panic and stress, and help you stay resilient during tough times. Furthermore, validating your emotions increases compassion and understanding of other people's strong feelings.

A simple way to validate your emotions is to notice what you feel and what you need. For example, when you feel angry you might need a quiet space to be alone for a few minutes, or when you feel lonely you might need to call a friend.

Practice using this simple sentence: I feel [emotion]. I need [mention a suitable action].

E.g., I feel confused about my math homework. I need to ask for clarity from my teacher.

Create five more sentences using the same format. For each sentence, mention a different emotion and action.

_____

_____

_____

_____

_____

_____

_____

_____

Exercise 15: Prepare for Overwhelming Situations

Strong emotions are sometimes caused by the fear of the unknown. For example, you may feel anxious about an upcoming presentation at school because you don't know what to expect. Preparing ahead of time and anticipating emotional discomfort can make you feel more comfortable facing the unknown.

Think about an upcoming event that is making you feel stressed and answer the following questions:

1. What event is about to take place? Describe the event in detail.

_____

_____

_____

_____

_____

_____

_____

2. How do you feel about the event? What emotions are being triggered?

_____

_____

_____

_____

_____

_____

_____

3. What is the worst-case scenario? What do you fear is going to happen?

_____

_____

_____

_____

_____

_____

_____

4. If the worst-case scenario occurs, what DBT skills can help you cope during and after the event? Make a list of at least three helpful exercises you have learned so far.

_____

_____

_____

_____

_____

_____

_____

5. Rehearse the event in your mind. Describe how and when you would practice the DBT exercises. For example, you might listen to your body—refer to exercise 3—before attending the event to gauge how you are feeling, and during the event, you might practice mindful breathing—refer to exercise 7—to regulate your emotions.

_____

_____

Taking the Opposite Action

In the heat of the moment, your default is to react out of rage or fear. You are more likely to act out of character and possibly say or do things that you might later regret. This is why DBT teaches a specific skill known as opposite action. As the name suggests, the aim is to do the opposite of what you are thinking or feeling when you are upset. For example, the opposite action when you are angry is to take deep breaths instead of yelling or slamming a door. Training your mind to take the opposite action can help you adopt positive behaviors in response to intense emotions.

Complete the following exercises to practice taking the opposite action:

Exercise 16: Go Against the Urge

Urges are the natural instincts that are triggered when you feel certain emotions, like rage or sadness. Depending on what behaviors you are accustomed to, you might get a strong urge to react in specific ways. For example, when you are sad, you might feel the urge to withdraw from everyone else. You may not even be conscious that you are behaving this way because it is your default behavior.

Learning to recognize and go against harmful urges can help to bring a sense of calm during stressful situations. Since some urges are unconscious, you can get in front of them by studying how you behave when triggered by certain emotions.

Take some time to reflect on your default behaviors when you are feeling angry, anxious, ashamed, and sad. Be as specific as you can be when noting your urges. Thereafter, think about the most suitable and realistic opposite action you can take. Make sure that the opposite action is simple enough to practice whenever you are triggered.

When I feel…	I get the urge to…	The opposite action is…
Angry		
Anxious		
Shame		
Sadness		

Exercise 17: Positive Activities Bucket List

To effectively take the opposite action, you will need to have a few positive activities to turn to whenever you feel overwhelmed. These activities don't need to be elaborate; they can be creative, relaxing, or productive ways to spend your time at home.

Create your own bucket list of positive activities. If possible, try to include at least one activity that is creative, relaxing, and productive. Combine a mix of indoor and outdoor activities, as well as a few that require planning, such as walking to the park. After creating your bucket list, challenge yourself to scratch off all the activities before the year is over.

Below are a few suggestions of what to include in your list:

Kick a ball	Cuddle a pet	Create a vision board	Complete a DIY project	Repeat positive affirmations
Take a bath	Doodle	Create a dance routine	Go for a swim	Do a random act of kindness
Bake cookies	Call a friend	Stargaze	Scrapbook	Volunteer

Write poetry	Watch a movie	Plan a picnic	Go hiking	Read a book
Journal	Go on a date	Practice yoga	Paint a picture	Plan a party

Exercise 18: ABC PLEASE

ABC PLEASE is a DBT acronym that teaches you eight positive actions to take when you are feeling overwhelmed. By the time you have completed all eight actions, you will feel calm and in control.

Go through the eight positive actions below, and write down a few suggestions you can try the next time you are upset.

1. **A: Accumulate positive emotions**

The more positive emotions fill up your day, the less affected you will be when presented with challenges. Make it your challenge to have at least two positive experiences each day. Try to incorporate experiences that align with your daily routine.

Write down at least 14 positive experiences—2 each day—that you can practice this coming week. If you enjoy the exercise, continue finding additional positive experiences to incorporate every week.

_____

_____

_____

_____

_____

_____

_____

2. **B: Build mastery**

The more competent you feel as an individual, the higher your confidence levels will be. The best way to increase competence is to work on your personal growth. Find one skill or hobby that can make you a smarter, healthier, or more creative person. Commit to practicing the skill or hobby regularly for the next month.

Write down the skill or hobby you have chosen and detailed steps on how to get started, such as what resources you will need, who you can ask for support, how much time it will require each week, etc.

_____

_____

_____

_____

_____

_____

_____

_____

3. C: Cope ahead

To prevent anxiety about the future, it is useful to have a list of healthy coping strategies that you can turn to whenever you are faced with specific obstacles. On the line space provided below, write down a few healthy coping strategies to deal with the following stressful events:

- getting a low grade on a test

- breaking up with your boyfriend/girlfriend

- succumbing to peer pressure

- feeling self-conscious about yourself

- family member falling sick

- not getting into the college/university of your choice

_____

_____

_____

_____

_____

_____
_____
_____

4. PL: Treat physical illness

Prioritizing your mental and physical well-being can help you detect and combat illnesses before they grow. Schedule regular appointments with your family doctor to check on your health. If you suspect that you may be living with a physical or mental illness, seek medical assistance immediately. While self-administered therapy is effective, it doesn't substitute a comprehensive treatment plan given by a qualified doctor.

5. E: Eat a balanced diet

The type of diet you consume can affect your physical and mental health. Research has shown that nutrient-rich diets based on whole foods can improve your moods, help you think clearer, and boost your immunity—lowering the risk of becoming sick (Mental Health Foundation, 2022).

Write down a list of your favorite proteins, whole grains, nuts and seeds, fruits, and vegetables. For the next week, challenge yourself to consume a diet that is based on these foods.

_____
_____
_____
_____
_____
_____
_____

6. A: Avoid mind-altering substances

Mind-altering substances, like alcohol, recreational drugs, and some prescription drugs, can make you more vulnerable to negative emotions. For example, alcohol is known to be a depressant that lowers brain activity and increases risk-taking. This means that if you are feeling angry under the influence of alcohol, you are likely to follow your urges because the logical area of your brain is not functioning as normal.

Underage drinking is a serious issue across the US and many parts of the world, which can lead to addictions and fatalities. If you have begun experimenting with illegal mind-altering substances, it is not too late to quit.

Create an action plan of how you can avoid mind-altering substances for the next month. Perhaps there are certain places, people, or activities you will need to distance yourself from. Your plan can also include creative ways to manage urges to use mind-altering substances. For example, when you feel like sneaking out to have a drink with friends, you can perform a hobby or work on a short-term goal. Speaking to your parents, a trusted teacher, or a counselor is another way to manage your urges and take the necessary steps to become clean.

_____

_____

_____

_____

_____

_____

_____

_____

7. S: Get sufficient sleep

According to the American Academy of Sleep Medicine, teenagers between the ages of 13–18 years should be sleeping for at least 8–10 hours in a 24-hour cycle (CDC, 2020). There are many factors that may be preventing you from getting adequate sleep, such as school demands, poor diet, undiagnosed mental illness, or battling with stress and anxiety. The excessive dependence on electronic devices can also interfere with your natural sleep cycle.

One way to improve your sleep is to get yourself on a bedtime routine. A bedtime routine consists of calming activities you practice every night, starting from about three hours before you go to sleep. Some of these activities may include taking a relaxing bath, reading a book, drinking chamomile tea, and turning off electronics.

Create your own bedtime routine with a minimum of five calming activities. Pick a specific time in the evenings to begin your routine. Make sure that all of your tasks for the day are complete and there are no interruptions.

_____

_____

_____

_____

_____

_____

_____

8. E: Exercise regularly

Physical exercise can improve your overall well-being. Studies have shown that regular exercise can improve your mental health and combat conditions like anxiety, depression, and ADHD. Incorporating physical exercise into your daily routine is also a great way to ensure you have consistent energy and balanced moods throughout the day.

What forms of physical activity do you enjoy? Create a seven-day workout plan to carry out for the next week. Set aside time each day to get active and break some sweat! At the end of the week, reflect on what you liked and disliked about your workout plan and make a few adjustments to motivate you to continue exercising regularly.

_____

_____

_____

_____

_____

_____

_____

_____

_____

Emotion regulation is a rewarding skill to learn. When you can control your emotions, you are able to think clearly before taking action. Rather than allowing strong emotions to overwhelm you, these skills teach you how to recognize and accept strong emotions, then take the opposite action!

Chapter 4:

Distress Tolerance Skills

If you are distressed by anything external, the pain is not due to the thing itself, but to your estimate of it; and this you have the power to revoke at any moment. —Marcus Aurelius

What Is Distress Tolerance?

Every individual has a stress tolerance level. This is the amount of distress they are able to bear before acting out of character. Most teenagers who struggle with emotion regulation tend to have a low tolerance of stress. After being slightly inconvenienced or challenged by another person, they will become defensive or emotionally shut down.

DBT, distress tolerance skills, help to increase your threshold of pain, so that you can remain calm, cool, and collected during stressful situations. The reason why these skills are so critical to learn is that they prepare you to face the real world. The truth of the matter is that you won't always find yourself in ideal circumstances, or surrounded by people who love and support you. Nevertheless, armed with distress tolerance skills you can find positive ways to cope with life's difficulties.

There are many different types of distress tolerance skills available to you. In the following sections, you will be taught three of these skills: self-soothing, improving the moment, and radical acceptance.

Self-Soothing

After you have been hurt, what happens to those intense emotions? Do you push them down and try to forget what happened? Or do you find ways to process and release your emotions?

Self-soothing is a DBT skill that encourages you to be your own therapist, rather than waiting on others to make you feel better. During and after a stressful situation, self-soothing techniques can help you cope with intense emotions and gently bring your body back to a normal state. You can think of it as providing the care that you need to restore a sense of safety and calm.

Complete the following exercises to practice self-soothing techniques:

Exercise 19: Calm Your Five Senses

Anxiety causes you to spend more time in your head than enjoying the present moment. In most cases, the anxious thoughts that go through your mind can feel more real than reality itself. However, continuing to entertain anxious thoughts only worsens your mental and emotional state.

Calming your five senses is a grounding technique that helps you gently pull your focus away from your thoughts and back to the present moment. The aim is to engage your five senses, namely: sight, smell, hearing, touch, and taste. The first step is to take a deep breath and look around the room. Next, challenge yourself to find:

- Five things that catch your eye visually.

- Four textures you can feel with your hands.

- Three sounds you can hear with your ears.

- Two scents you can detect with your nose.

- One taste you can recognize with your mouth.

Don't rush through this exercise. Take your time and enjoy the break from overthinking.

How did you find the exercise? Record your experience below:

_____

_____

_____

_____

_____

_____

_____

_____

Exercise 20: TIPP

TIPP is a DBT acronym that stands for "temperature, intense exercise, paced breathing, paired with muscle relaxation." It is suitable to practice when you are in an ongoing crisis and seek to regulate your mind and body. Below are the four steps to practice TIPP:

1. T: Temperature

Lowering your body temperature can be calming when you are feeling overwhelmed. The best way to do this is by running your hands under ice water, chewing on a block of ice, taking a cold shower, or pressing a cold and damp towel on your forehead. If you have any medical conditions, consult your doctor before adjusting your body temperature.

2. I: Intense exercise

Strong emotions create a surplus of energy inside of you. To prevent this energy from being used destructively, you can perform intense physical exercise to safely release it. Intense exercise can be any sport or form of cardio that increases your heart rate and allows you to break a sweat. Examples include 30-minute aerobic workouts, running on a treadmill, playing tennis, or any other action sports.

3. P: Paced breathing

Deliberately slowing down the pace of your breathing can help you regain a sense of control. Focus on taking longer and fuller breaths through your nose that reach your belly. Take a short pause before slowly releasing your breath out of your mouth. You can also focus on counting while breathing to maintain a consistent pace.

4. P: Paired with muscle relaxation

Muscle relaxation is a technique that helps you identify and release physical tension throughout your body. Similar to the body scan, start from the crown of your head. Identify the major muscle groups, such as the face, shoulder, chest, arms, and legs, and practice squeezing and releasing each muscle. Notice how you feel after releasing the grip.

How did you find the exercise? Record your experience below:

_____

_____

_____

_____

_____

_____

_____

_____

Exercise 21: Practice the Half Smile

Research has shown that smiling releases tension in the face and calms your nervous system. It can also trick your brain into believing you are happy and trigger the release of endorphins—also known as happiness hormones. Even a fake smile has been found effective in reducing stress and lowering the heart rate (Patnaik, n.d.).

Whenever you sense panic or stress setting in, take a deep breath, relax your face, and gently make a half smile with your lips. Your lips should be slightly turned upward in a natural position. Continue to take deep breaths in and out of your nose. Count up to 10 then relax your lips. Check-in with yourself to see how you are feeling.

You can also practice holding a half smile while thinking about a distressing situation or during conversations with difficult people. You can use the half smile as a distraction or delay tactic to prevent you from losing control of your emotions.

Improving the Moment

There are times when you are placed in difficult situations that you can't escape. For instance, you may be experiencing ongoing family conflict or constant pressure at school, which doesn't seem to end. As the name suggests, improving the moment is a DBT skill that can help you cope with ongoing stress. It teaches you how to accept what you can and cannot control, and do whatever is within your power to improve the moment.

Complete the following exercise to practice improving the moment:

Exercise 22: IMPROVE

The acronym IMPROVE can help you find positive activities to offset negative life circumstances. You can think of these activities as positive distractions to avoid anxious thoughts and increase emotional resilience.

Below are seven ways to IMPROVE stressful moments:

1. I: Imagery

When your real-life circumstances aren't looking up, you can use mental imagery to envision positive outcomes. Find a quiet space where you can lie down and practice visualization. Close your eyes and imagine your current life situation positively changing. Envision solutions being found for those problems that seem hopeless and everything coming together.

You can also envision yourself becoming a stronger and more confident version of yourself; someone who can withstand the present challenges in your life. Spend at least 10 minutes each day on this exercise, each time visualizing different positive aspects of your life situation.

2. M: Create Meaning

You can change your emotional response to life circumstances by changing how you think about them. In other words, by assigning a different meaning to what you are currently experiencing, you can feel better about yourself and your life situation.

The simplest way to do this is to create a positive meaning to what is unfolding in your life, regardless of how negative it may look. Think about the benefits of being in that situation, such as the potential life lessons you can walk away with. The most important part about creating meaning is to fully convince yourself that what you are going through will turn out to be in your best interests.

Think about a challenging life situation that won't seem to go away. Write down five benefits that can come out of this situation. Make sure that what you write down is believable, so that you can slowly start to change your perception.

\
\
\
\
\
\
\
\

3. P: Prayer

In moments of distress, you can close your eyes and say a heartfelt prayer. Prayers are simple messages of hope and gratitude that are directed toward a Higher Power. They symbolize letting go of the constant fight to figure out your life on your own terms and seeking help from a higher source of wisdom.

Write a short prayer that you can recite whenever you are feeling overwhelmed. If you don't have a Higher Power, such as a belief in God or a supreme deity, you can address the prayer to your wise mind.

\
\
\
\
\

_____

_____

_____

_____

_____

4. R: Relaxation

Another way to improve the moment is to turn to your favorite relaxation exercises. What's great about these exercises is that they work on calming the mind and body, simultaneously. For example, taking deep breaths allows more oxygen to the brain, which helps to calm the mind. However, it also allows more air into your lungs and leaves you feeling at ease.

Write down a list of 5–10 relaxing exercises that you can turn to in times of distress:

_____

_____

_____

_____

_____

_____

_____

_____

5. O: One thing in the moment

Doing one thing at a time is a mindfulness practice that can reduce stress and overthinking. The aim is to completely immerse yourself into the single task you are doing. Whenever your mind drifts, gently pull it back to the task at hand.

To practice focusing on one thing at a time, grab a fruit and place it on a plate. Go through the steps of eating the fruit, such as peeling, dicing, chewing, and swallowing it. To ensure you stay focused on the task, keep your five senses engaged. Consider how it looks, smells, feels, and tastes.

6. V: Vacation

Taking some time away from a stressful situation can help to relieve tension. If it is not practical for you to take a vacation, look for ways to create healthy distance from the situation or person who may be troubling you.

For example, if you are having a difficult time relating with your parents, find a quiet room or area in the house or in the garden where you can retreat whenever you want to spend time alone. Taking a vacation can also include taking a break from social media, social clubs, sports, and other commitments that may be exposing you to stress. Set aside a reasonable length of time that you will be "away" and use that time to focus on your mental well-being.

7. E: Encouragement

During stressful periods of life, you can become your biggest cheerleader by practicing positive self-talk. Get into the habit of speaking words of encouragement that can boost your self-esteem and combat negative thinking. You can create positive affirmations that specifically address areas of your life where you lack confidence. Remember to write your affirmations in the present tense and focus on your strengths.

Think about an area of your life where you need upliftment. Write five positive affirmations such as "I am…" to encourage yourself. Set aside time in the mornings and evenings to recite your positive affirmations while looking into a mirror.

_____

_____

_____

_____

_____

_____

_____

_____

_____

_____

Radical Acceptance

Radical acceptance is about coming to terms with how things are in your life. Whether you are in a good space or struggling to get by, you always have the option to accept your reality as it is.

In order to practice radical acceptance, you must drop any judgment you might have about your life. Instead of wishing things were different, living with regrets, or feeling discouraged because of what you don't have, you simply learn to love your life as it is.

Please note that radical acceptance isn't the same as turning a blind eye to abuse or making excuses for people's bad behaviors. You are encouraged to make the most of your life, but continue taking steps to protect your space and build healthy relationships.

Complete the following exercises to practice radical acceptance:

Exercise 23: Acceptance Mantras

Every now and again, you need to be reminded to accept your life circumstances as they are. Acceptance mantras can help you do just that! What makes acceptance mantras different from positive affirmations is that they are usually short and direct sayings that help to disrupt negative thinking and reset your mind. Instead of simply making you feel good, they are effective in inspiring positive actions.

To create acceptance mantras, start by writing down a list of situations outside of your control. For example, you can't control your siblings' attitude, parents' health status, whether you are accepted into your college of choice, or how other people think of you.

_____

_____

_____

_____

_____

_____

_____

For each situation outside of your control, create a short and direct response that shows radical acceptance of it. For example, when you worry about the hurtful things someone says about you, the mantra could be "I cannot control how other people view me." This mantra can inspire you to immediately think about something more productive. Other examples of mantras you could create include:

- My life isn't perfect, but it is good.

- I have everything that I need.

- Everything will naturally unfold with time.

- I am not in a rush.

- I am doing the best I can.

_____

_____

_____

_____

_____

_____

_____

_____

Exercise 24: Positive "What If's"

In general, when we create "what if" scenarios, we think about the worst thing that can happen. However, the truth is that "what if" scenarios can be positive. Instead of only looking at what could possibly go wrong, you can look at what could possibly go right.

In the table below, think about unpleasant situations you are currently dealing with. For each situation, create a negative and positive "what if" scenario. The purpose of this exercise is to show you that life can be experienced from two perspectives, and you get to choose which perspective to adopt.

Unpleasant Situation	Negative "What If?"	Positive "What If?"
E.g., I am currently not speaking to my best friend.	What if we go weeks without speaking and our friendship ends?	What if this time of no contact is helping both of us reflect on what went wrong?

Unpleasant Situation	Negative "What If?"	Positive "What If?"

Exercise 25: Fact vs. Opinion

When you are distressed and feeling emotional, it can be difficult to look at your situation non-judgmentally. You might confuse opinions with facts and create a false picture of reality.

Before accepting your beliefs as the truth, see whether they are based on facts or opinions. If they are based on facts, there will be sufficient evidence to validate your beliefs, whereas if they are based on opinions, you may only have your emotions to draw from. Whenever you come across beliefs that are based on opinions, adjust them to match reality.

Consider whether the statements below represent facts or opinions. If you come across statements which represent opinions, rewrite them to match reality.

Statement	Fact	Opinion	Rewritten Opinion
I'm not smart enough.			
I got a "C" for my test.			
I won't survive this.			

Statement	Fact	Opinion	Rewritten Opinion
Nobody likes me.			
I'm struggling to make friends.			
My siblings hate me.			
I have a hard time managing my emotions.			
My sleeping patterns are irregular.			
My family doesn't understand me.			

Exercise 26: Proactive Problem-Solving

Radical acceptance doesn't mean giving up and allowing bad situations to get worse. If you are able to do something to improve your current life circumstances, then you ought to. Being a proactive problem solver is part of learning how to make the most of your life.

Think about a problem that you are capable of doing something about, then answer the following questions:

1. What problem are you currently dealing with?

_____

_____

_____

_____

2. Who else is involved in this problem?

_____

_____

_____

_____

3. Break the problem into small steps that you will need to solve. For example, what will you need to do first, second, and third to address the problem?

_____

_____

_____

_____

4. What role can the other people involved in this problem play? Which action steps can they assist with?

_____

_____

_____

_____

_____

5. Write down as many ideas to address each step of the problem. Think of small and practical solutions that are within your control.

_____

_____

_____

_____

6. What aspects of the problem are outside of your control? Which parts aren't you able to fix? How can you practice acceptance for those parts?

_____

_____

_____

_____

7. Look back at the answers you have come up with. Decide on the plan of action moving forward. Be specific about what problem you are trying to solve, who will help you solve the problem, what action steps you will take, etc.

_____

_____

_____

_____

Distress tolerance skills cannot make your troubles disappear, however, they can improve the way you approach challenges. Notice that the change happens inside of you, instead of your external environment. This means that while your external environment may continue to look chaotic and stressful, you can develop the necessary coping skills to move through life differently.

Chapter 5:

Interpersonal Effectiveness Skills

No one can make you feel inferior without your consent. —Eleanor Roosevelt

What Is Interpersonal Effectiveness?

One of the most important skills to learn is how to communicate effectively with others. Relationship building is an activity that begins with the strong bond you form with your parents as a child and continues to include various relationships with extended family members, friends, teachers, coaches, and one day your work colleagues.

Interpersonal effectiveness is a DBT skill that teaches you how to nurture relationships, make requests, stand up for yourself, and set healthy boundaries. All of these strategies are learned through mastering the art of effective communication. If you have ever found yourself feeling afraid to express your needs or communicate hurt feelings, then you may need to brush up on a few interpersonal effectiveness skills.

The following exercises will teach you how to listen attentively and positively resolve conflict and boundary violations.

Attentive Listening Skills

To become a better communicator, you must be able to listen carefully to what others are saying. Listening helps you accurately receive what is being communicated and respond with an appropriate message. Attentive listening is about paying attention to the verbal and nonverbal language that is being passed to you. Not only are you able to hear what is being told, but you can also read the other person's body language.

Complete the following exercises to practice attentive listening skills:

Exercise 27: Quiz on Listening Skills

Are you an effective listener? Take this short quiz to find out!

Read through each statement and circle the most appropriate number. The numbers represent the following answers:

4: Almost always

3: Usually

2: Seldom

1: Never

After completing the quiz, tally your points to find the results.

Statements	Almost always	Usually	Seldom	Never
Do you wait until someone has finished speaking before you respond?	4	3	2	1
Do you encourage others to finish their train of thought when they hesitate?	4	3	2	1
Do you wait until others have fully expressed their ideas before sharing your opinion?	4	3	2	1
Are you able to still listen to someone speak, even when you dislike them?	4	3	2	1
Are you able to listen carefully regardless of how someone speaks, i.e., has a strong accent, uses poor grammar, etc.?	4	3	2	1

Statements	Almost always	Usually	Seldom	Never
Do you stop whatever you are doing and maintain eye contact when someone is speaking?	4	3	2	1
Are you able to put your thoughts aside and focus on what someone else is sharing?	4	3	2	1
Do you ask open-ended questions to ensure you understand what someone is saying?	4	3	2	1
Do you often paraphrase/repeat what someone said to make sure you heard correctly?	4	3	2	1
Do you listen with the intention of discovering how someone else is feeling in the moment?	4	3	2	1
Totals for each column				
Grand total =				

Determine your results:

Score between 36–40: Excellent listener!

Score between 30–35: Good listener—learn to ask more questions and paraphrase the other person's message to gain more clarity.

Score between 26–29: Sharpen your listening skills—practice making eye contact and pay attention when another person is talking.

Score between 0–25: Go back to the drawing board—practice listening without interrupting midway or getting sidetracked with your own thoughts or judgments.

Exercise 28: Pick Up Nonverbal Cues

Research shows that 55% of communication is nonverbal (University of Texas, 2020). This means that listening to words alone isn't enough to fully understand what another person is thinking or feeling. You will need to study their nonverbal cues, such as their facial expressions, gestures, and body language to accurately interpret what others are saying.

Below are a few scenarios designed to increase your awareness of nonverbal cues. Go through each scenario and think about what the nonverbal cue might be communicating.

1. A group of people is talking loudly next to a student who is trying to study. The student gives a loud sigh, packs up her books, and moves to a nearby table. What might she be feeling?

_____

_____

_____

_____

2. A mother comes back home after work to find the house in a mess. None of her kids have completed their household chores as instructed. She spends the rest of the evening giving everyone at home the silent treatment. What might she be feeling?

_____

_____

_____

_____

3. A group of friends are sharing personal stories about their past experiences. One friend decides to share a story that involves another member of the group. The other member gives the speaker a serious look but says nothing. What might they be feeling?

_____

_____

_____

4. A teacher is standing in front of the class and presenting. All of a sudden, she increases the volume of her voice. What might she be feeling?

_____

_____

_____

_____

5. Two friends are having a conversation. One of them yawns and starts tapping their foot. What might they be feeling?

_____

_____

_____

_____

Communicating Effectively

Effective communication is about expressing ideas and thoughts clearly and directly to avoid misunderstandings. This allows the listener to understand what you need and act accordingly. The secret to effective communication is to first think about what you want to say, then package your message in a way that can be easily received by others.

Complete the following exercises to practice communicating effectively:

Exercise 29: Set Healthy Limits With Others

One of the requirements to build strong relationships is to be able to express your likes and dislikes with others. This kind of feedback is meant to help other people learn more about you, and the kinds of behaviors you find acceptable or unacceptable. The DBT acronym DEAR MAN can help you share deep thoughts and feelings, and set healthy limits with others.

Think about a recent unpleasant behavior done toward you by a friend, teacher, or family member. Follow these steps to have an honest conversation about that incident:

1. D: Describe the offense

Describe the behavior that you disliked. Focus on the specific behavior, rather than attacking the person.

_____

_____

_____

_____

2. E: Express how it made you feel

Use the information you learned about primary and secondary emotions in chapter 3 to describe how the behavior made you feel.

_____

_____

_____

_____

3. A: Assert your needs

Be clear about what you need from the other person moving forward. Don't be afraid to set boundaries, such as making it known what you will not tolerate. This is your moment to stand up for yourself and draw healthy limits with others.

_____

_____

_____

_____

4. R: Reinforce

Are there any benefits or improvements that will occur if your needs are met? Share these with the other person. Moreover, let them know what consequences they will face if your needs aren't met—e.g., what will happen if they violate your boundaries.

_____

_____

_____

5. M: Mindful

List a few mindfulness exercises you can practice during the conversation to help you stay focused on getting your message across. For instance, you might take regular deep breaths, maintain eye contact, etc.

_____

_____

_____

6. A: Appear

Think about a few nonverbal gestures or body language that you can display to appear more confident. For instance, you can stand up tall, uncross your arms, make a half smile, etc.

_____

_____

_____

7. N: Negotiate

Be open to the possibility of negotiating. This isn't required when giving honest feedback, but may come in handy when expressing how you would like others to behave moving forward. They may or may not be comfortable with your suggestions and will therefore seek to negotiate. Before entering any negotiation, create a list of non-negotiables—things you will not agree to regardless of the other person's viewpoint.

Exercise 30: Resolve Conflict FAST

It's normal to get into disagreements with the people closest to you. This is because even though you love each other, you have different needs and expectations. When conflict arises, you have three choices on how to respond: You can either respond with aggression, bottle your feelings, or communicate how you feel and make a peaceful resolution. The last option demonstrates a high level of self-respect. When you are able to voice your frustrations respectfully and set clear limits with others, you can prevent misunderstandings in the future.

The DBT FAST acronym can help you resolve conflict peacefully and respectfully. Below are four steps to get started:

1. **F: Be fair**

Before approaching the other person to resolve conflict, take a moment to reflect on what exactly happened. Look at the situation from different perspectives to see the bigger picture. Being fair is about admitting the role you played in the conflict while also holding the other person accountable for their mistakes.

Recall a recent conflict you entered with a friend or family member. Describe what happened from your perspective and the other person's perspective.

2. A: Apologize

You owe the other person an apology if you have hurt them. However, you don't need to apologize for making requests, having different opinions, or disagreeing with them. If you are going to give an apology, make it sincere.

Mention the specific actions you regret and the negative impact they had on the other person—e.g., "I am sorry for yelling at you over the phone. I know that it was disrespectful and it hurt your feelings." Note that you can also request an apology from someone if they hurt your feelings. Make your request specific, such as "I would like an apology for the way you spoke to me during recess."

_____

_____

_____

_____

_____

_____

_____

_____

3. S: Stick to your values

Be clear about why certain behaviors are unacceptable. Mention the values that were violated by the other person. For example, if you value kindness, someone who raises their voice at you or spreads rumors behind your back goes against that value. Think of three recent situations where your values were disrespected. Describe how those certain behaviors went against your values.

_____

_____

_____

_____

_____

_____

_____

_____

4. T: Be truthful

When resolving conflict, be honest about how you feel. Remember, if the other person cares about you, they will respect your needs and boundaries. Avoid telling lies or making exaggerations to make the other person look or feel bad. Simply speak from your heart and allow them to choose how to respond.

Exercise 31: Overcome Resistance

Have you ever tried to explain your point of view and noticed the other person becoming defensive? This is a natural way that some people respond to confrontation. To avoid this type of reaction, it is important to resolve conflict compassionately. One way to approach this is by acknowledging and respecting the other person's perspective.

After sharing your concerns, listen attentively to the other person. Validate their opinions to show that you respect what they have to say. A simple phrase you can use is "I hear what you are saying, and I think/feel…"

For instance, you might say "I hear that your feelings were hurt too, and I think we may have misunderstood each other's intentions." Adding an "and" shows that you can validate someone while maintaining your independent thoughts and feelings.

Practice using the validation statement to resolve the following disagreements:

- You feel taken for granted by your friend. They feel like you are being overly sensitive.

- You think that your parents' new rules are too strict. They think that you are challenging their authority.

- You feel like spending time working on your hobbies over the weekend. Your friend feels like you are deliberately avoiding them.

_____

_____

_____

_____

_____

_____

_____

_____

_____

Interpersonal effectiveness skills focus on getting your thoughts and emotions across with clarity and confidence. Note that you won't always agree with your friends or family members, but when you are able to communicate effectively, you can work through misunderstandings and find common ground.

Conclusion

You don't always need a plan. Sometimes you just need to breathe, trust, let go, and see what happens. —Mandy Hale

Adolescence is the passage of time when you transition from a child into a young adult. That is why this particular stage of your life can feel overwhelming. Nevertheless, with the right coping skills, you can endure through the challenges of adolescence and come out successful!

What makes DBT such an effective therapy is the fact that it reinforces important life skills, such as how to manage stress, control your emotions, or communicate effectively with people. Moreover, the four skills mentioned in this workbook won't just help you get through the rough patches, but they will also teach you healthy coping strategies to improve your overall well-being and maintain a positive outlook.

The exercises shared with you are introductions to mindfulness, emotion regulation, distress tolerance, and interpersonal effectiveness. Practicing these exercises on an ongoing basis will improve the way you manage stress and cope with the highs and lows of everyday teenage life.

The important message to take away from this workbook is that every emotion is temporary. What you feel strongly in this moment will naturally subside until you cannot sense that feeling anymore. Knowing that your emotions are temporary should be a reminder that you are bigger than your big feelings. You are always in control of how you respond to and overcome various life events.

Dear Reader,

Thank you for choosing to read my workbook. I sincerely hope it has provided you with valuable insights and practical guidance on your personal development journey. Your feedback is incredibly important to me.

If you found this book helpful or thought-provoking, I kindly request that you consider sharing your thoughts through a review. By doing so, you can help others discover the book and make an informed decision about whether it alights with their needs.

Leaving a review is quick and easy. You will just require your smartphone or tablet to scan the QR code below. This will take you to the review page for this workbook, and from there all you have to do is select a star rating, leave an honest review and click submit.

Your review will not only help me grow as an author but will also assist other individuals seeking guidance on their personal development journeys.

I appreciate your time and support. Thank you for being a part of this transformative experience.

Best regards,

Richard Bass

About the Author

Richard Bass is a well-established author with extensive knowledge and background on children's disabilities. Richard has also experienced first-hand many children and teens who deal with depression and anxiety. He enjoys researching techniques and ideas to better serve students, as well as providing guidance to parents on how to understand and lead their children to success.

Richard wants to share his experience, research, and practices through his writing, as it has proven successful for many parents and students.

Richard feels there is a need for parents and others around the child to fully understand the disability or the mental health of the child. He hopes that with his writing people will be more understanding of children going through these issues.

Richard Bass has been in education for over a decade and holds a bachelor's and master's degree in education as well as several certifications including Special Education K-12, and Educational Administration.

Whenever Richard is not working, reading, or writing he likes to travel with his family to learn about different cultures as well as get ideas from all around about the upbringing of children, especially those with disabilities. Richard also researches and learns about different educational systems around the world.

Richard participates in several online groups where parents, educators, doctors, and psychologists share their success with children with disabilities. Richard is in the process of growing a Facebook group where further discussion about his books and techniques could take place. Apart from online groups, he has also attended training regarding the upbringing of students with disabilities and has also led training in this area.

A Message from the Author

If you enjoyed the book and are interested on further updates or just a place to share your thoughts with other readers or myself, please join my Facebook group by scanning below!

If you would be interested on receiving a FREE Planner for kids PDF version, by signing up you will also receive exclusive notifications to when new content is released and will be able to receive it at a promotional price. Scan below to sign up!

Scan below to check out my content on You Tube and learn more about Neurodiversity!

References

Ackerman, C. E. (2017, December 29). *Interpersonal effectiveness: 9 Worksheets and examples (+ PDF)*. PositivePsychology.com. https://positivepsychology.com/interpersonal-effectiveness/#what-interpersonal-effectiveness

Buckloh, L. M. (2018). *5 Ways to know your feelings better (for teens) - KidsHealth*. Kidshealth.org. https://kidshealth.org/en/teens/emotional-awareness.html

CDC. (2020, September 10). *Sleep in middle and high school students*. Www.cdc.gov. https://www.cdc.gov/healthyschools/features/students-sleep.htm#:~:text=Importance%20of%20Sleep&text=The%20American%20Academy%20of%20Sleep

DBT Self Help. (n.d.-a). *IMPROVE the moment*. https://dbtselfhelp.com/dbt-skills-list/distress-tolerance/improve/

DBT Self Help. (n.d.-b). *Reduce vulnerability with ABC PLEASE*. https://dbtselfhelp.com/dbt-skills-list/emotion-regulation/abc-please/

DBT Self Help. (n.d.-c). *Ride the wave*. https://dbtselfhelp.com/dbt-skills-list/emotion-regulation/ride-the-wave/

DBT Self Help. (n.d.-d). *TIPP: Changing your body chemistry*. https://dbtselfhelp.com/dbt-skills-list/distress-tolerance/tipp/

Dialectical Behavior Therapy. (n.d.-a). *Coping ahead*. DBT. https://dialecticalbehaviortherapy.com/emotion-regulation/coping-ahead/

Dialectical Behavior Therapy. (n.d.-b). *DBT : Wise mind - skills, worksheets, videos, and activities*. DBT. https://dialecticalbehaviortherapy.com/mindfulness/wise-mind/

Dialectical Behavioral Therapy. (n.d.). *Describe your emotions*. DBT. https://dialecticalbehaviortherapy.com/mindfulness/describe-your-emotions/

Good Reads. (n.d.-a). *DBT quotes (23 quotes)*. Www.goodreads.com. https://www.goodreads.com/quotes/tag/dbt

Good Reads. (n.d.-b). *Emotional regulation quotes (13 quotes)*. Www.goodreads.com. https://www.goodreads.com/quotes/tag/emotional-regulation

Good Reads. (n.d.-c). *Marcus Aurelius*. Www.goodreads.com. https://www.goodreads.com/author/show/17212.Marcus_Aurelius

Good Reads. (n.d.-d). *Matthew McKay*. Www.goodreads.com. https://www.goodreads.com/author/show/98986.Matthew_McKay

HMA. (2016). *Skilful listening - Listening questionnaire*. https://www.hma.co.nz/wp-content/uploads/2016/01/SKILFUL-Listening-Listening-Questionnaire.pdf

Hoshaw, C. (2022, March 29). *What mindfulness really means and how to practice*. Healthline. https://www.healthline.com/health/mind-body/what-is-mindfulness

Johnston, E. (2022, March 16). *What are "I feel" statements?* Verywell Mind. https://www.verywellmind.com/what-are-feeling-statements-425163#:~:text=%22I%20feel%22%20statements%20communicate%20how

Klynn, B. (2021, June 22). *Emotional regulation: Skills, exercises, and strategies*. Www.betterup.com. https://www.betterup.com/blog/emotional-regulation-skills#:~:text=With%20emotional%20regulation%20skills

Mal Paper. (2021, November 12). *72 Mindfulness quotes for daily inspiration and motivation*. Mål Paper. https://malpaper.com/blogs/news/72-mindfulness-quotes-for-daily-inspiration

Mental Health Foundation. (2022, January 25). *Diet and mental health*. Www.mentalhealth.org.uk. https://www.mentalhealth.org.uk/explore-mental-health/a-z-topics/diet-and-mental-health

Patnaik, T. (n.d.). *Surprising health benefits of smiling*. Mpowerminds.com. https://mpowerminds.com/blog/surprising-health-benefits-of-smiling

Retnasaba, G. (n.d.). *Negative judgments*. DBT. https://dialecticalbehaviortherapy.com/mindfulness/mindfulness-of-negative-judgments/

Salters-Pedneault, K. (2021, September 13). *Accepting emotions when you have BPD will improve your health.* Verywell Mind. https://www.verywellmind.com/how-accepting-emotions-can-improve-emotional-health-425368

Schimelpfening, N. (2023, February 24). *What is Dialectical Behavior Therapy (DBT)?* Verywell Mind. https://www.verywellmind.com/dialectical-behavior-therapy-1067402#toc-benefits-of-dialectical-behavioral-therapy

SkillsYouNeed. (2011). *Listening skills.* Skillsyouneed.com. https://www.skillsyouneed.com/ips/listening-skills.html

Taproot Therapy. (2018, December 18). *DBT skills: The 6 core mindfulness skills.* Taproot Therapy NYC. https://www.taproottherapynyc.com/blog-dialectical-behavior-therapy-skills/dbt-skills-the-6-core-mindfulness-skills

Tewari, A. (2021, May 11). *107 Highly empowering quotes to boost your self-worth.* Gratitude - the Life Blog. https://blog.gratefulness.me/20-great-quotes-to-boost-your-self-worth/

Tsangarides, L. (2023, February 16). *Celebrities who have found DBT useful.* Mindful Healing. https://www.mindfulhealingllc.com/blog/celebrieties-who-have-found-dbt-useful

Tull, M. (2020, July 17). *Distress tolerance in post traumatic stress disorder.* Verywell Mind. https://www.verywellmind.com/distress-tolerance-2797294

University of Texas. (2020, November 3). *How much of communication is nonverbal?* UT Permian Basin Online. https://online.utpb.edu/about-us/articles/communication/how-much-of-communication-is-nonverbal/#:~:text=It%20was%20Albert%20Mehrabian%2C%20a

Image References

Cameron, J. M. (2020). *Photo of girl using black smartphone* [Online image]. Pexels. https://www.pexels.com/photo/photo-of-girl-using-black-smartphone-4144288/

Cottonbro Studio. (2021). *Group of friends having fun sitting on skate park* [Online image]. Pexels. https://www.pexels.com/photo/group-of-friends-having-fun-sitting-on-skate-park-10118237/

Danilevich, O. (2020). *Teenagers taking a groupfie* [Online image]. Pexels. https://www.pexels.com/photo/teenagers-taking-a-groupfie-4762767/

Kindel Media. (2021). *Woman in blue shirt talking to a young man in white shirt* [Online image]. Pexels. https://www.pexels.com/photo/woman-in-blue-shirt-talking-to-a-young-man-in-white-shirt-8550841/

Lach, R. (2021). *Smiling girls in small group of teenagers on walk on forest footpath* [Online image]. Pexels. https://www.pexels.com/photo/smiling-girls-in-small-group-of-teenagers-on-walk-on-forest-footpath-10484693/

Lusina, A. (2021). *Sad teenage girl lying on bed* [Online image]. Pexels. https://www.pexels.com/photo/sad-teenage-girl-lying-on-bed-7269383/

Miroshnichenko, T. (2020). *Woman in white sweater sitting and praying on bed* [Online image]. Pexels. https://www.pexels.com/photo/woman-in-white-sweater-sitting-and-praying-on-bed-5199748/

Pavlikovsky, B. (2021). *A woman playing an electric guitar* [Online image]. Pexels. https://www.pexels.com/photo/a-woman-playing-an-electric-guitar-7715705/

Riva, E. (2016, September 29). *Rain umbrella drops* [Illustration]. Pixabay. https://pixabay.com/illustrations/rain-umbrella-drops-water-rainy-1700515/

Smith, J. M. (2017). *Man wearing green printed crew neck shirt while sleeping* [Online image]. Pexels. https://www.pexels.com/photo/man-wearing-green-printed-crew-neck-shirt-while-sleeping-296817/

Summer, L. (2021). *Multiracial ladies having disagreement in light room at home* [Online image]. Pexels. https://www.pexels.com/photo/multiracial-ladies-having-disagreement-in-light-room-at-home-6383204/

Zimmerman, P. (2020). *Upset woman listening to therapist* [Online image]. Pexels. https://www.pexels.com/photo/upset-woman-listening-to-therapist-3958421/

Made in United States
Troutdale, OR
08/06/2023